THE SPOTT

John Clarke

Plum Tree

First Published by Plum Tree Publishing Ltd 2005

Plum Tree Publishing Limited,
Worcester,
England, WR7 4NX

Printed and bound in Great Britain

ISBN: 0-9533646-2-3

A catalogue record for this book is available from the
British Library.

Cover image by Brian Smith
Photo on opposite page courtesy of George Higginbotham
Photo on rear cover courtesy of Elizabeth Clarke
Photo on page 73 courtesy of Pamela Clarke

CONTENTS

Introduction

'The Spotted Flycatcher'

Gray on gray post, this silent little bird
Swoops on its prey – prey neither seen nor heard!
A click of bill; a flicker; and, back again!
Sighs Nature an Alas? Or merely, Amen?

(Walter de la Mare)

Introduction

I first came across the Spotted Flycatcher in 1979. Finally able to realise my dream of being more involved in wildlife and conservation, one of my first actions was to make and put up a series of bird nest-boxes in the fields and woods around our house. In one small copse we fastened a half coconut shell in the ivy on a tree – my nest-box manual advised that it might attract Pied Wagtails. In the first year it was taken by a pair of Spotted Flycatchers and I have been fascinated by them ever since. In my naive enthusiasm I thought that this was my first ornithological discovery – only to find later that the flycatchers' attraction to coconut shells had been known for at least thirty years!

This small book tells of a research project into the Spotted Flycatcher – a bird in serious decline in Britain. News of a bird population in serious decline is all too common these days – that research is being carried out also comes as no surprise. What makes this project so different – perhaps unique – is that in some instances almost entire local village communities have over a four year period participated in an ambitious scheme to monitor the fortunes of this endearing small bird.

The project was not planned to be so large or so complex. The original idea was to ascertain how many pairs of Spotted Flycatcher still nested in four local villages. In order to publicise the survey a few posters were made and put up in local shops and churches, and a short article was published in church magazines. The response was amazing, far more

Photo John Clarke

Spotted Flycatchers love coconut shells! This was my first nest in 1979. I have tried various designs based on the shell but keeping it simple seems to work for the flycatchers. The survey suggests that adding supports and a roof may make it more visible and accessible to predators. Simply drill a half shell with drainage and fixing holes and wire or screw it to a wall or climbing shrub so that the foliage partly hides it. A climbing rose is ideal cover, not dense, thick foliage. If the shrub threatens to engulf the shell, prune it lightly so that the birds can fly in. Do not clean out the shell or cut back the shrub once the young have fledged because the flycatchers may have a second brood. My theory is that the birds can save time and energy by using the shells and merely building a 'lining' rather than the entire nest base and wall.

widespread than anticipated, and it was the extent of the enthusiasm that eventually made the survey so difficult – and at one point almost impossible. The tidal wave of support dragged in a further five villages and now I was searching nine in all – albeit with extra help. The number and distribution of study pairs increased – and so too did the effort required to monitor all the nests. In the end I was averaging more than 220 nest visits (in addition to searches) per annum! 2004 was very difficult – we still checked nine villages and found 33 pairs to monitor, but poor weather conditions and a high predation rate meant that many nests failed and even more time was needed to relocate the birds as they made second and third attempts to breed.

Fortunately with so many helpers, in most years it was possible to locate nearly all of the pairs and then to follow their fortunes as the season progressed. Some pairs were lucky – their initial nesting attempt was successful and if time permitted and they were still in good condition they would lay another clutch of eggs, usually in the same nest (after a few repairs). Many were not so lucky and were forced to abandon the nest at building stage, eggs or young were lost to predators – or, in periods of bad weather, the young died of starvation or hypothermia. Those that failed once found a new site (which we had to locate) and tried again – many tried three times before finally being successful. Sadly, each year a few gave up after two or three failed attempts and prepared themselves for the long trip back to Africa.

The exhausting work of surveying was tough but so too was the emotional, human side as many people struggled to come to terms with the loss of their particular nest. I spent a lot of time on the telephone and making extra 'house calls' to discuss the losses. On several occasions each year I almost gave up, but fortunately each dreadful event seemed to be countered by some uplifting incident or news and we carried on.

Then, as the summer ended, local groups of Spotted Flycatchers would be reported feeding up on insects and supplementing their diet with elderberries, and then suddenly they were gone. It would be almost nine months before we saw them again.

This book reports on the survey, provides summarised data from the research and compares it with information from other sources. The data looks at clutch size, egg fertility and fledging success whilst recording in detail the nest site and the habitat selected. In addition, the book is able to record, sometimes in anecdotal form, observations on the birds' behaviour made by a great many households from the nine villages involved. But just as importantly, it also records the human part of the story – how people of all ages and backgrounds were and still are affected by the Spotted Flycatcher, how they wait each year for them to arrive back from their wintering grounds in Southern Africa to these gardens in the Cotswolds, how they try to protect them from predators, provide nesting sites and cooperate closely with the researcher. Some are old friends of the Spotted Flycatcher, others have only recently got to know them - surprisingly few, if any, were indifferent.

Whilst the data is important, the human side is fascinating, even moving. This book seeks to demonstrate the important practical role that local communities can play in wildlife conservation. Given the opportunity, they responded as a team and network and without them this project would have failed. If the Spotted Flycatcher were to disappear from this area of Britain it would not be because nobody cared – and it would be sorely missed.

The Bird

Description

The Spotted Flycatcher (*Muscicapa striata*) can easily be overlooked by those who don't know about it. After all, it is only here for just over three months each year, arriving later than most other migrants – and after many other species have already bred at least once. Most gardeners and birdwatchers have got used to the spring birds that have settled into their territories when, often unseen, the Spotted Flycatcher arrives. Its song is barely noticeable and there are no bright colours or markings to distinguish it from other 'brown', smaller birds. And it is no use looking out for a 'spotted' bird because the Spotted Flycatcher is more 'streaked' than 'spotted'. However, flycatcher enthusiasts know when and where to look out for these delightful little birds and few arrivals are greeted with such excitement. Like the sound of the first cuckoo or the sight and sound of screaming swifts returning to the nest sites, the unassuming flycatcher also stirs the soul.

In size, it is the same length as a robin, slightly smaller than a chaffinch and vaguely like a dunnock (or hedge sparrow). At a distance it appears uniformly grey-brown on the back, with a paler front and underside. Closer up, the grey-brown is slightly enriched by warmer brown areas with pale streaks on the wings, whilst the paler head and breast are clearly

Muscicapa striata, the scientific name for Spotted Flycatcher provides a better description than 'spotted'. The adult has small streaks on the throat and breast but the fledged young are more spotted in appearance.

marked with darker streaks. The feet and legs look quite black, the bill (or beak) is very noticeably black and pointed. In silhouette the bird appears slim and perches in a distinctive, very upright position – usually in prominent places, such as on posts, wires, dead branches, TV aerials and washing lines. Its legs are slightly shorter than those of similar birds because it spends little time on the ground. When it does land the take-off may be slightly undignified as its longish wings cannot perform a full sweep.

Once you have watched a Spotted Flycatcher catching flies it becomes much more distinguishable. The bird appears motionless on its perch but it is constantly scanning for prey – flying insects from mosquito-size to large butterflies. It appears to be selective and once it spots a potential victim it seems to explode into action. It can swoop upwards, downwards or sideways to intercept or chase down the victim before returning to its favourite perch to eat it. The wings of some larger insects and remarkably, the stings of bees, are removed by wiping the insect backwards and forwards on the perch. Extraordinarily, it appears to be able to distinguish between a bee and a similarly marked hoverfly, which is not subjected to such treatment. The speed and agility of the hunting bird is amazing. It can hover like a humming bird for several seconds, plummet to within a few centimetres of the ground or rocket skywards to catch its prey.

Many summer migrants and British resident birds rely heavily on beetles and caterpillars for feeding their young. Even the pied flycatcher (*Ficedula hypoleuca*), the only other British flycatcher species, rears its young mainly on larvae of Lepidoptera (*BWP*). The Spotted Flycatcher relies mostly on flying insects and therefore delays breeding until insect numbers begin to peak – in June and July.

Status

The UK Spotted Flycatcher population has been in serious decline for a long time – numbers have fallen by 80% over the past 30 years. The causes are less certain. In my area, in addition to the villages the bird was formerly found in old orchards, along woodland edge and in glades, and in open scrub with trees. In 1986 O'Connor and Shrubb reported Spotted Flycatcher as favouring lines of trees and hedgerow trees. Fuller (1982) surveyed 23 woods of less than 10 hectares and found Spotted Flycatcher breeding in 70%. Out of 40 woods of 20-40 hectares they were breeding in 80% and were breeding in 90% of the 36 woods of 80-160 hectares. Since 1994 I have not recorded them at their former sites or indeed anywhere on farmland or woodland around my study area - and they now seem confined to the villages. The loss of many orchards, changes in woodland management and structure, and the use of pesticides on neighbouring land may all have contributed to the change. It is possible that Dutch Elm disease, which resulted in the loss of thousands of elms in this area, may also be a factor.

Spotted Flycatchers spend most of their lives either travelling or resting in their 'winter' quarters. On migration they face many new as well as traditional threats. Modern climate changes appear to be affecting the spring weather in Europe and expanding the deserts on the African continent, whilst droughts and wars ravage some wintering areas.

The risks of travelling through countries where birds are shot or trapped for food or sport have been known for many years. Modern mist nets and traps greatly increase the dangers for migrants, and where the species travels in a series of short 'hops' rather than long-distance flights the likelihood of being killed by man is surely increased. *The Migration Atlas* admits to certain biases in the data but provides some startling statistics on flycatcher mortality. The data is based on information gleaned from recoveries of dead, ringed birds. Of 111 birds found in Britain 60% of the deaths were attributed to "human-related causes" and 30% to "domestic predators". Of 42 deaths in Spain, 86% were "taken by man". "Man" took all 23 dead birds reported from Portugal and Morocco.

In Britain it is clear from anecdotal evidence that the Spotted Flycatcher population is not just affected by changes on the farm or in the woods, it is also declining in the villages – a great many residents can remember the birds formerly nesting regularly in their gardens but not in recent times. Here too, at least some causes may lie in the wider environment – air pollution, climate change and pesticides may also be reducing prey populations. It is also possible that the reduction in 'pest control' and loss of many gamekeepers over the past fifty years may have led to an increase in predators. Grey squirrel (*Sciurus carolinensis*) and magpie (*Pica pica*) are now very common in village gardens and have been seen predating nests, including those of Spotted Flycatcher. Most houses now have central heating and hundreds of redundant chimneys are colonised by jackdaw (*Corvus monedula*) which predate nests and fledglings of many other birds. The havoc wreaked on nesting birds by the domestic cat (*Felis catus*) is well documented.

It is also interesting to consider what effect an increasing population of other species of garden-nesting birds might have on the Spotted Flycatcher. Casual observations indicate that there is fierce competition for the nest sites between a number of species. Spotted Flycatchers like to nest in thin cover against walls and fences and by the time this late migrant arrives, blackbird (*Turdus merula*), song thrush (*Turdus philomelos*), mistle thrush (*Turdus viscivorus*), dunnock (*Prunella modularis*), house sparrow (*Passer domesticus*), robin (*Erithacus rubecula*), wren (*Troglodytes troglodytes*), woodpigeon (*Columba palumbus*), pied wagtail, (*Motacilla alba yarrelli*), greenfinch (*Carduelis chloris*), goldfinch (*Carduelis carduelis*) and chaffinch (*Fringilla coelebs*) may have built nests there whilst blue tit (*Parus caeruleus*) and great tit (*Parus major*) use nest-boxes on the same walls. There have been instances where blackbird and woodpigeon have used the lid of a Spotted Flycatcher box for their own nest base! Perhaps the provision of feeding stations for birds throughout the year encourages more to breed in our gardens but also increases competition with and disturbance to nesting flycatchers. It is also likely that the increased density of breeding birds in our gardens attracts more predators away from their 'natural' hunting areas in the wider countryside.

Habitat

The more 'traditional' or 'natural' Spotted Flycatcher habitats are described above. However, in the study area the flycatcher is now only to be found in the villages, within which the diversity of trees, shrubs, hedges, lawns and borders, the houses clad in shrubs, creepers and climbers, and the proximity of small ponds and streams offer excellent hunting and nesting habitat. On most days the pairs, who rarely stray far from the nest area, are able to find a sheltered part of the garden in which to feed. However, periods of cold, wet and windy weather can be just as disastrous here as in the natural sites. Observations found that many villages had an area, sometimes quite small, which attracted several pairs of flycatcher, whilst few pairs were found outside it. The reasons for this are not yet clear.

The Breeding Season

The first birds arrive back in the study area during the second week in May – the 10th is the earliest recorded date. The main influx appears to take place during the last two weeks of May, with some birds arriving in early June. In 2004 a few pairs arrived in the second week of June and were located in three of the villages. Despite thorough searches these late pairs were not found earlier so it would appear that their migration had been delayed by bad weather or that they had tried and failed to set up territories elsewhere before moving to the study area. The latter option seems less likely as this study showed that 'failed' pairs rarely moved far from their original territory before trying again.

Few pairs begin nest building before the last week in May, and even fewer manage to start egg laying before the end of the month. Nest building begins in earnest in early June and may take as few as three or four days to complete (those nesting in coconut shells appear to take less time). The nest is built mainly of moss and spiders' webs with some fine grasses, and then lined with feathers. It is interesting to note that few observers have seen flycatchers collecting and carrying nesting material – the birds can be very secretive at this stage, and observations suggest more prone to disturbance and more likely to desert. If building is abandoned the birds invariably find a new site – usually within 100m but sometimes as close as 5m to 10m – and start again. The causes of failure noted by observers at this stage include building maintenance work, gardening activities, human social activities (sunbathing, al fresco meals, barbecues etc) and disturbance by other bird species or 'visits' by predators (such as squirrel, magpie etc).

Once the nest is complete, egg laying begins and one egg is produced each day, usually in the earlier part of the morning. Early clutches have four or five eggs but replacement clutches drop to three or four whilst second clutches (after earlier fledging success) usually consist of three. Incubation begins when the last egg is laid and usually lasts between 11-15 days (more often 12-14 in this study). The young are born naked and blind and require a great deal of 'brooding' by (in this study) the female. This means that for a few days at least the male does most of the hunting for the family, the female coming off for brief periods to feed and preen. Having emerged from an egg less than 2cm long, the young grow rapidly, and in good weather will be ready to fledge (leave the nest) after 12-14 days. However, the adults may continue to feed them for up to three weeks after fledging. Sometimes this means that the adults may be repairing and re-lining the nest – or even starting a second clutch of eggs – before their first brood is independent. All this physical energy is fuelled by eating insects so flycatchers begin feeding as soon as suitable prey appears in the morning and continue throughout the day. On warm evenings they have been seen feeding long after other birds have gone to roost.

During this study it was observed that fledged families appeared to gather in small feeding groups and at the end of the breeding season they formed larger groups of up to 20 birds. As they tended to move to parkland and woodland edge, inside or outside the villages, and often fed high up in the tree canopy, locating groups was usually a matter of luck

Photo John Clarke

Sometimes, you can't even stop for a photograph!

and counting was very difficult. These 'post-fledging' or 'pre-migration' groups have been found at several villages and it is assumed that each local cluster of pairs form into specific groups – but of course, there is no scientific basis for this.

The groups of flycatchers are building up condition and moulting prior to migration (*BWP*) and it is now that their diet appears to change. Once more, observations rather than scientific data provide the evidence but early in the season the birds have been observed taking mainly 'brown' butterflies (including small tortoiseshell and peacock) but rarely 'whites'. However, during this pre-migration period they take any species – one gardener was delighted when in a matter of a few hours flycatchers killed all the white butterflies that had been egg laying on his cabbages! There were many observations from different villages of Spotted Flycatchers eating elderberries during this period. In fact they have been seen to gorge themselves to such an extent that one was observed regurgitating surplus fruit!

At some time in late August/early September the birds disappear and thereafter only single stragglers are recorded from the villages – the latest, exceptional date being 9th September.

Migration

Why do they do it? Well, researchers believe that the birds require a certain minimum number of daylight hours to find enough food from a high population of flying insects, so as the African autumn and winter approach they follow 'summer time' as it moves north, setting out on the return journey as the European autumn sets in. Not a great deal is known about precisely where the 'British' population of Spotted Flycatchers go in winter but it is known that birds from western Europe head south across the Mediterranean, through North Africa, across the deserts, heading for southern Africa. European birds have been found as far south as South Africa, with others in south-west Africa and across as far as Zimbabwe and Zambia. *(BWP)*

I am grateful to several members of the British Trust for Ornithology (BTO) who know something about the Spotted Flycatcher as it moves on migration. Ringing studies (where birds are caught, measured and weighed and then fitted with a tiny metal ring so that if found dead or re-caught the data can be compared), have shown that unlike many species the Spotted Flycatcher does not put on large amounts of fat reserves before travelling considerable distances in one go. The flycatchers apparently feed up and then move in short 'hops' (The Migration Atlas). This method must considerably reduce their rate of progress but may have other advantages since they feed on flying insects and have even been seen feeding in deserts. However, this strategy increases the risks from man (see pages 8 & 9) and from habitat degradation en route.

I am told that northern birds appear to move down the west coast of Britain and cross to northern France from Cornwall. It is more likely that the Worcestershire and other Midlands birds cross the channel from Dorset. (Kester Wilson pers. comm.)

During the European winter

Most of the birds winter well south of the equator, where they utilise a wide range of habitats including scrub, scattered trees, woodland edge, disturbed ground, parks and even reed-beds. Many birds do not arrive back on the wintering grounds until October to November – the birds wintering farthest south have only December to February to recover before setting out on the three-month journey back to Europe (BWP). This hazardous lifestyle, where up to six months each year is spent travelling – often in hostile environments and conditions – may well be a factor affecting the decline of Spotted Flycatcher populations.

Roberts reports that in southern Africa the Spotted Flycatcher is usually solitary and the birds are known to use the same winter sites year after year. Their 'wintering' habitats include 'savanna, open woodland, orchards, gardens, parks, exotic plantations'. There they use low perches – often below 2m – for hunting. They are described as feeding on a wide range of flying insects, some ground insects such as ants and termites and also on small berries. Interestingly, they appear to manage without water when it is unavailable and this may explain the lack of observations of flycatchers seen drinking during the Worcestershire survey.

The Villages

The names and precise location of the villages will not be disclosed here. Suffice to say, they usually contain a mixture of houses and buildings, some built of that wonderfully warm Cotswold stone, some traditional black-and-white, part-timbered, and others of old-style brick – quite a few are still thatched. In most villages a few modern houses have sprung up and in some, 1950s-style council houses have been added. Most of the villages within the study area contain some wonderful old properties – including churches, farmhouses and grand buildings with huge gardens, some with orchards, parkland and shrubberies. They have evocative names, such as The Manor, The Court, The Vicarage, The Grange, The Old Farmhouse – titles that promote historical images of the villages themselves. One of my favourites is an old Georgian manor set in 11 acres of grounds with two walled gardens, croquet lawns, stables and river frontage. Towering redwood and cedar trees overshadow the acacias and yews, ringed by smaller shrubs and wonderful herbaceous borders. Many of the properties boast tennis courts and large swimming pools. Fruit trees, fences, nets and croquet hoops make perfect flycatcher perches! Forget the people, this is the ultimate Spotted Flycatcher habitat. Modern gardeners use few chemicals and with shelter provided by walls and trees, the scented spring and summer air is alive with flying insects – flycatcher heaven!

A walled garden (containing shrubs, fruit trees, flowering plants), and beyond it a churchyard (no chemical sprays, tombstones for perches, shrubs and shorter grass). To the right and behind – part of a small area of parkland provides shelter and alternative feeding. Spotted Flycatcher heaven!

Occasionally, the most sought after properties (in flycatcher as well as house agent terms!) may be home to three pairs of Spotted Flycatcher – and this phenomenon is not unique to our villages. In *The Bird Man* the author recalls having up to twenty pairs of the birds nesting on one wall at the family seat in the Borders during the 1940s.

That is not to say that flycatchers are not attracted to smaller properties: our cottage is a two-up two-down, 400 year old building with a smallish garden. However, because it is adjacent to a shrubbery and taller trees our garden is a sun-trap and attracts many insects – and hence flycatchers which nest by the door.

The nine villages vary considerably in size, the smallest comprising less than 30 properties and the largest more than 250. At least one of the villages is almost wholly owned by one estate. This provides a certain continuity to property management and subsequently, in certain aspects, to flycatcher habitat.

Several of the villages are built along small streams and watercourses and where these pass through gardens they become a 'feature' – in the form of pools, waterfalls and cascades.

And this is the point where people, properties and flycatchers come together in this project – no more so than where the house-owner can employ a gardener. Gardeners around here often know their birds well and one or two have been incredibly successful in locating Spotted Flycatchers at their various customers' properties. Moreover, they are there regularly to observe and monitor not just the birds but also factors that may be affecting breeding success or failure.

As in many other country areas of Britain, there is a tendency for properties to be bought or rented by wealthier people from big cities, some of whom are used to more 'open plan', manicured gardens – particularly in areas where large trees are seen more as a potential legal minefield, in a society likely to sue if a conker falls on one's head! They may not share the views of their predecessors that planting large shrubs and trees retained the landscape character of their village whilst sheltering their gardens. So, in a few places dead and dying trees are removed, all creeper and ivy within the garden (so good for insects and nesting cover) are removed rather than managed, and thus good flycatcher habitat is lost. Similarly, old orchards now known to be rich habitat for wildlife are abandoned as uneconomical or sold for development. Many properties, though, still retain that rich diversity of garden habitats and thus attract birds like the Spotted Flycatcher.

All this does not mean that the Spotted Flycatcher is a Cotswolds bird – far from it. Contacts around Britain report them in similar village garden habitats from Norfolk to Wales, in southern England and north into Scotland. However, here we are only concerned with the cluster of nine villages in the study area.

The People

The Community

It would be true to say that most low to middle-income people can no longer afford to live in these villages. Exceptions include those in council properties, retired estate workers and families in 'tied' cottages, but the villages tend to be inhabited largely by the comfortably off and the wealthy. Many retired people and modern-day commuters have made their homes or second homes here. Some run their businesses from home. Few of the traditional village pubs and shops remain and one or two large 'catchment' schools now replace a network of village institutions. But outwardly, the villages change little – if at all – and some of the wildlife, particularly birds, so affected by rapid change in the surrounding countryside, are still drawn here and welcomed by most households.

These then are the people who play host to the flycatchers. Over the four years of the survey I have been made welcome by so many – some of them have become good friends. I have been enormously impressed by the commitment and support given to me – and to the birds themselves. I look back with great and fond admiration as I recall here some members of the 'Flycatcher Gang', as it was sometimes known.

The Flycatcher Gang

My favourite characters include :

The retired and rather 'proper' spinster who stopped me in the street and whispered mischievously, "How do I join your gang? I've never been in one before – it's very exciting!"

The gardener who tracked down Spotted Flycatchers in several of his customers' gardens each year. He has a brilliant eye and great observational skills and knows the birds and their behaviour as well as anyone I have met. If he telephoned to say that, based on a fleeting glimpse, he thought there might be flycatchers at a property I soon learned to get there as soon as possible – in the four years he never got it wrong.

The pensioner who spends much of his income on feeding birds in his garden – some even follow him indoors! He was incandescent with rage when jackdaws raided his local flycatcher nest and will by now, I am sure, have wreaked terrible vengeance on possible culprits!

As a result of the study, several people became aware of the number of attacks on birds' nests in their gardens by grey squirrel and magpie and decided that an annual cull would help protect the flycatchers during the breeding season.

The lady who, realising that her flycatcher coconut shell nest-box was unstable, fixed beneath it a small dog basket with a blanket lining. On two occasions she 'caught' a nestling, warmed it up again and replaced it in the nest! All the youngsters fledged successfully. She also had an amazing relationship with the female Spotted Flycatcher which trusted her completely and would feed the young, completely unconcerned, when she was standing by the nest. The bird also obliged by 'posing' for photographs but when I tried would have none of it – until the lady came and stood with me. On one occasion, still worried about the wobbly nest, the lady came out at night to see if all was well. Carefully she shone a torch – and there was the parent, standing on the side of the nest guarding her young and showing no sign of alarm. It is true; I have seen the picture! However, it is not a recommended course of action – this was a unique and special relationship and not one other bird/person formed such a bond during the study.

The following year, by the time the lady had remembered to do something about the unstable nest-box the birds had arrived and were well on with nest-building. Unsure of what to do, but reasoning that if the nest fell down the birds would need somewhere else quickly, she got the gardener to site a second box of improved design about ten feet away. We were all amazed to discover a day or two later that the birds had literally moved their nest by dismantling it and re-building in the new site!

Another lady came back from a morning's shopping to find that she had shut a flycatcher in the house when she left. The bird allowed her to pick it up and carry it to the front door where she released it. The bird flew straight to the nest (by the door) and continued her incubation! All eggs hatched and the young fledged successfully.

One person who felt that the local Spotted Flycatcher food supply was being depleted by the weather put out a dish of old cat meat which was quickly colonised by flies. The pair of flycatchers nesting nearby took full advantage of the temporary but welcome bonanza!

I advised one enthusiast that the open-fronted box that he had made and put up may not be right – the opening was very wide and perhaps he could reduce it. Imagine my surprise to find later that a pair was nesting in the box which now sported a small pair of 'curtains' made from an old chamois leather!

A lady phoned early one morning to tell me that her Spotted Flycatcher nest had been predated. Her tears were not uncommon as people get extremely attached to the flycatchers. But this was different – the predator was her own cat. She repeatedly apologised to me and felt she should have protected the nest better. I was struck by her honesty in admitting the real cause: although painful to her it provided important information.

A happier cat story was told me by another lady: she came downstairs one morning to find that hers had brought in a newly-fledged Spotted Flycatcher. Its first flight from the nest high above the door had gone disastrously wrong and it had been scooped up by the cat and brought in via the cat flap. The small bird was a lot easier to pick up than the live mice usually left as a breakfast offering. A neighbour brought a long ladder and the terrified baby was returned to the nest but having officially 'fledged' it would have none of it and gamely leapt out again! This time it successfully flew a few yards, landing in a tree, whereupon its parents and siblings who were still around came and collected it.

I was told the story of several ladies from a number of villages who were sat together in church waiting for a funeral to start. "By the way," whispered one suitably-hatted lady to her neighbours, "Did you know that - - - has lost her flycatchers?" "Oh no!" exclaimed the others in unison, shattering the sombre silence in the church. Fortunately, nobody enquired as to what might be wrong!

Some builders were renovating a house and local villagers reported to me that Spotted Flycatchers were nesting above a window. I bravely approached and explained my study, fully expecting to be laughed at – or worse. How wrong I was – the burly five left their tea break and followed me round to have a look via my mirror-on-a-stick ... I can still hear the chorus of "Ah!" and "Oh look!" as they saw the four nestlings – blind and naked and each no bigger than a little finger nail. I left with the distinct feeling that if anyone – just anyone – went near that nest, they would be in BIG trouble!

I was called to one property by the gardener, who had seen Spotted Flycatchers. I searched the creeper and roses on the house wall, probed ivy on trees and along the garden wall to no avail. When I reached the bottom of the garden, some steps led down to a small terrace with a 'grotto' dug into the bank. The cleaning tools for maintaining the large swimming pool were leaning against the wall and there on the broom head was the flycatcher nest! Problems were foreseen as the house-owner was due home and wished the pool to be cleaned and prepared for what was forecast to be the first hot weekend of the year and a party had been planned. We explained about the flycatchers and my project and he immediately ordered that the pool remain covered for a further three weeks until the young had safely fledged.

One man called me to see a nest on the end of a roof joist in the dormer window of an upstairs room. During each visit to monitor the nest he had to move furniture around so that

Spotted Flycatcher's nest on a broom head (see story in text). Notice how the spiders' webs help to bind together the bits of moss and dried grasses – but also help to camouflage the nest.

I could lean precariously out of the window with my 'mirror-on-a-stick' to see into the nest!

A fledgling 'gang member' was visiting some open gardens elsewhere in the Cotswolds when he noticed there were Spotted Flycatchers around. He pointed them out to the owner who was not familiar with the bird. Feeling by now a little more confident our man then pointed out to the owner where on his property they might well nest. At least one of them was hugely impressed when they subsequently found two occupied nests!

At least two households set up 'viewing stations' with telescopes at a safe distance from their nests. They and their neighbours were able to watch the young being fed and eventually fledging.

Because of nesting Spotted Flycatchers, barbecues were moved, house repairs delayed and gardening jobs postponed – occasionally an alternative house door was brought into use while the birds nesting close to the main door settled in. And that was something that we all learned – once the people and the flycatchers had got used to each other the birds would tolerate a great deal of human activity close to their nest.

These are not isolated stories about a tiny number of 'oddballs' or 'eccentrics' – it goes much deeper and wider than that. These people do not feel that watching a few nature programmes on the telly and being an RSPB member is enough – they find themselves actively involved, putting themselves to some inconvenience, genuinely caring and trying to understand the complexities of wildlife conservation. Surprisingly to some, they come from all walks of village life and all backgrounds – perhaps this project has taught us more about people than Spotted Flycatchers?

Initial Responses

The following are a few of the typical responses when I knocked on doors asking for help and access to gardens:

The Newcomer – possibly new to village life – and birds – but no less supportive.

"The Spotted what?"

"Spotted Flycatcher. I'm carrying out research ... overwinters in south-west Africa ...three months to get here ... blah blah ... 80% decline in twenty years ... seems to like these villages ... blah blah ... getting people to help ... blah blah".

"So, how can we help?"

"Well, ... blah blah."

"OK, great, do you want our phone number? Come round whenever you like – if we're out etc. What was it called again – spotted what?"

"Flycatcher ... Spotted Flycatcher!"

"We have spotted woodpeckers."

"No, it's the Spotted Flycatcher!"

"Fascinating – and quite small you say? I must tell my children when they get home – and my husband at the weekend", (or vice versa). "We'll look it up in the children's bird book. Good luck – and if we see a little brown bird doing whatever it was you said they did, shall we give you a ring?"

The Standard Resident – considerable knowledge of garden birds – may or may not have noticed or indeed encountered the Spotted Flycatcher.

"Spotted Flycatcher. I'm carrying out research … overwinters in south-west Africa … three months to get here … blah blah … 80% decline in twenty years … seems to like these villages … blah blah … getting people to help … blah blah.

"Oh yes, I've heard of it – and you – you're the bird man aren't you?"

"No, well yes, some people call me the 'Flycatcher Man'".

"Flycatcher Man! Yes, that was it – great, how can we help?"

"Well, … blah blah."

"Great, I'll look it up again. My friend says they've got them at the Manor. Is that right?"

"Yes, they're very excited about it."

"Great, well come round whenever you need to and if we see one we'll give you a ring."

The Flycatcher Enthusiast – knows the bird well. It nests or has nested on the house wall in the past.

"Spotted Flycatcher ... research ... decline ... help ... blah blah."

"Oh wonderful! I've heard about you – isn't it great – what's gone wrong, we used to see so many?" At this point, accusations levelled at farmers, chemicals etc are discussed – still declining in gardens – problems on migration and in Africa etc.

"Well, we're really glad that you are doing this – our favourite bird – it's so sad – can we help by asking friends etc? Come round whenever you like. We'll walk around the village and let you know if we see any."

The Ever-so-slightly Cynical

"The spotted what?"

"Spotted Flycatcher. I'm carrying out research ... blah blah."

"Hmmm."

"There are several pairs in this area and I'm wondering if some are nesting in your garden."

"Hmmm."

"So, I was wondering if I might take a look."

"Hmmm ... What is that?"

"Oh, that's my mirror-on-a-stick. I can search for nests and then look in without using a ladder. Ladders can be noisy and disturb vegetation – using them takes longer and disturbs the birds more."

"Oh, right. Do you do this sort of thing for a living?"

"Yes. Well, no. I am a conservation advisor and sometimes my work involves research. This project is different because I'm doing it for myself – and it relies on help from the local community."

"Hmmm, right, well you'd better come in and have a look then. What did you call it, the spotted what?"

"Flycatcher – Spotted Flycatcher! Look, there's one!"

"Where?"

"On that dead twig."

"Good God! How did you spot that? How can you tell?"

"Well, blah blah ... shape ... silhouette ... see the way it flies."

"Good God! Why is it sitting there?"

"Possibly because its mate is on a nest nearby. That's the sort of place – in the wisteria over that window. I'll just have a look. Oh! There she goes! Here's the nest, just where the branch bends over. If I hold the mirror like this you can just see the four eggs."

"Good God! How did you do that? How did you know? So we have a pair! I'll just fetch my wife – she loves her birds. What do we do now? What was it called again – the spotted what?"

The Survey

Targets

The aims of the survey were first to find all the pairs of Spotted Flycatcher and secondly to monitor their breeding throughout the season. To do that I needed to find the birds, locate their nest sites and then check the nests for details of egg laying, clutch size (number of eggs), brood size (number of young hatching), and then the number of young fledged (that successfully flew). I could also record details of nest sites and learn about nesting and feeding habitats – and territories. From this information I could calculate averages and compare with national statistics.

Finding the birds

Surveying birds may take the form of counting species in your garden but most often involves walking 'transects' in suitable habitat – field edges, wetlands, woodlands or wild moorland. Surveyors do not usually come into contact or become closely involved with people, but in this project the surveys could not have taken place without whole communities being involved, and so-called standard scientific methods of surveying were not applicable.

During the first two years of the study – or at least until most residents had got used to seeing me wandering up and down the road - there was always a risk of being arrested! Imagine looking out of your front window and seeing a stranger, armed with a pair of binoculars and a mirror on a long, extending handle, hanging around outside and peering intently at your house. What would you do? In the event, some people came out to check up on me while passers-by stopped to ask politely what I was doing. On hearing my explanation most were very interested but a few went away leaving me with the distinct feeling that they felt I needed therapy of some sort!

As the original concept included just four small villages, the plan was simple. In each village a local flycatcher enthusiast was identified and we systematically searched our own patch by walking the roads and literally peering into gardens! At any property where 'Spotted Flycatcher Potential' was deemed to be high, doors were knocked on and house-holders' permission sought before carrying out a more detailed search.

Having practised the previous year, I felt more confident of the methodology, and so, often accompanied by my wife Pamela whose ears and eyes are much sharper than mine, I actually searched all four villages. However, as the project rapidly expanded to nine villages the time required increased dramatically and I relied heavily on my network of 'spies'. These local representatives introduced me to many householders. With the threat of burglary in our area security is a high priority. I was amazed therefore when almost everyone gave me complete freedom of access to their property. In four years I was only refused entry twice – one person, uniquely, did not wish to take part but nevertheless did let me know that a pair of Spotted

Photo John Clarke

Creeper-clad walls, a variety of trees and shrubs, flower beds and lawns provide nesting and feeding habitat within a radius of just a few metres for Spotted Flycatchers. Hunting perches range from croquet hoops to television aerials and are rarely more than 25m from the nest. Unless bad weather forces them to do otherwise the birds appear to prefer to stay within sight of the nest. For birds that feed on flying insects this is very restrictive. Swallows and martins will fly considerable distances to collect food while swifts may hunt many miles from their nests. However, the Spotted Flycatcher does not carry a 'bolus' of prey items – rather individual catches in its beak – so the further it has to travel the more energy expended and hunting time lost.

Flycatchers were nesting in his garden. The other owner refused at first on the understandable grounds of security, but joined in for the last three years. Many requested a visit after being introduced to me by neighbours or reading about the survey in their Parish Magazine.

At least two main searches were made each year and, as word spread and more people joined in, the basic searches were made easier. Eventually around 120 households were looking out for Spotted Flycatchers – but only about one in four each year would be lucky enough to host a pair.

Locating the nests

Once a pair was found it was important to locate the nest site as soon as possible. If the pair was nest building or feeding young it was easier – I could hide somewhere and watch them fly in with nest material or food. However, Spotted Flycatchers can be very secretive while nest building and observers may spend a great deal of time lurking in bushes or peering out from garden sheds! Quite often it was the house-owner (and frequently the gardener) who would spot activity and call me out, thus saving a great deal of time.

Once located, details about the nest – its height above the ground, its position, the actual nest site and what stage the nesting had reached were recorded. I swapped contact details with the householder so that they could keep me up-to-date with any changes.

Sometimes locating the nest came down to what is known as 'cold searching'. In other words, based on instinct and experience you search all suitable nesting habitat on the house and around the garden.

Monitoring the nests

Nest building takes between three days and a week depending on the site and on whether the birds are refurbishing an old nest. One egg is laid per day until the clutch is complete (up to five eggs in this survey) and then incubation begins immediately and lasts for about twelve to

Typical Spotted Flycatcher eggs – five is almost certainly a first clutch of the season. (Above) The egg colouring and markings varied little in the 200 or so nests that I have seen. Then in 2002 and again in 2004 – in the same village – a bird laid blue eggs with no markings. (Below) At first I thought it possible that the flycatcher had taken over the nest of another species but the fledglings were definitely Spotted Flycatchers. Interestingly, the three blue clutches found were all of three eggs. A fourth nest, that I believe held a second brood, had three fledglings.

fourteen days. After hatching, the young grow rapidly and are ready to leave in a further twelve to fourteen days. In order to obtain data on all stages a minimum of five visits was required. Of course, the actual monitoring took just a few seconds but the 'visit' lasted much longer as people invariably wanted feedback on progress, advice on protecting the nest – or indeed information about other wildlife in their garden. If the nest failed or was predated the race was on to find where the pair would make another attempt. If the nest succeeded, it would still require checking to see if they attempted a second brood. Replacement nests and second broods were linked to the original as this provided important information about the birds' breeding behaviour.

In addition to the numerous house or site visits made as I searched for pairs of Spotted Flycatchers, hunted for replacement nests and checked for second broods, I made an average of around 220-250 actual nest visits each year.

Processing the data

As the situation changed daily it was important to keep all records up-to-date. At the height of flycatcher breeding there could be around thirty nests to monitor with several more to locate, while searches for more pairs continued. As the nests were started at different times, visits to check laying, hatching and fledging dates could not be coordinated and on busy days I would have to visit five or six villages. At the end of each day the information collected was entered on a summary sheet containing brief details of every nest. In addition a loose-leaf file was compiled, with a section for each village and a page for each nest site. Here the details of the householder, the nest habitat and site details were kept. Each visit was recorded together with details of findings.

At the end of the breeding season and after a short break I returned to the data. Each year the data was summarised and a short report produced and distributed to all who took part. The data was then transferred onto specially designed 'Nest Record Cards' produced by The British Trust for Ornithology. This well-known charity was founded in 1933 and has been collecting breeding data for most British birds since 1939. BTO members send in thousands of records each year and these are held on the Trust's computer. At the end of 2003 they were holding 11,271 nest records for Spotted Flycatcher – the 'Flycatcher Gang' has contributed 185 of them. In the results for this project I quote comparisons between my data and what the BTO has found over many years.

In addition, as part of a project to study more fully the fortunes of breeding birds throughout the season, the BTO has instigated a trial scheme called 'The Constant Nest Monitoring Scheme'. Volunteers agree to designate a 'plot' or area and choose a species. Within that plot they try to locate all the breeding pairs for their species and to follow their breeding attempts. This scheme is very similar to my Spotted Flycatcher project and so, although my plots were extremely large (whole villages!!), our data was contributed in 2003 and 2004.

Watercolour by the author

Results, Comparisons and Conclusions

Overview

To many, four years might seem a long time to be studying a local population of Spotted Flycatcher, but that depends on what the survey set out to prove. If we had been looking at long-term changes in breeding success or breeding behaviour the study would ideally last for twenty years. That would be fine for the young ornithologist who could tailor the research to available time and resources. In this case, the aims were never that high – not least because by the end of a twenty year study the main researcher and several of his supporters would be well into their eighties!

As the project depended heavily on the cooperation of so many people, whose response and contribution could not be forecast, aspirations needed to be modest. So, the original plan was merely to assess the distribution and population of the Spotted Flycatcher in the local villages – and little else. However, almost as soon as it started it became apparent that the research could be widened to look at breeding in greater detail. Moreover, the data could include information about nest sites and breeding habitat. Such was the quality of support for the project that in the second year we were able to start 'Constant Nest Monitoring', which meant that each pair of birds was monitored throughout the season – through successive breeding attempts – adding greatly to the value of the research. In addition, dozens of supporters, most with no preconceptions about the research, were able to provide anecdotal observations about the birds, considerably increasing available knowledge. The annual reports brought several responses from across the country – from those who monitor the fortunes of their local pair of flycatchers, from others who knew the birds but were unaware of their decline, and from some who have now formed small research groups to monitor their local populations.

So, what started out in 2001 as a modest survey grew into a major, local study of a bird in serious decline. Thanks to the local communities this possibly unique type of research has added greatly to our knowledge of Spotted Flycatcher breeding and behaviour, whilst simultaneously raising public awareness of this and other species in decline. However, it would be wrong to claim to have had the scientific foresight required in order to produce these results – they are more the product of a happy accident.

Results – breeding status and success

Nest Data for the four years is detailed in the Appendix but to summarise:

- A total of 137 pairs were found – of which 122 could be studied.
- 182 nests were located – of which 170 were studied.
- Although more than 120 households supported the study the birds bred at only 72 properties.
- In order to monitor accurately, about 1,000 nest visits were made.

Photo Courtesy Tommy Holden

Adult Spotted Flycatcher (left) with a fledged youngster. The fledgling has reached this size in a little over two weeks since emerging from an egg less than 2cm long, fed almost exclusively on flying insects. It may appear that the flycatchers could be disadvantaged by such an exclusive diet at a time when other birds are feeding on a seasonal glut of caterpillars and ground insects, which are available in most weather. However, in reasonable conditions when the insects are on the wing, the flycatchers will not face competition from other species.

- 34.6% of nests failed at egg or young stage (national average per BTO is 32.8%). The BTO does not include failures at nest stage but this survey includes 'substantial nest' (ie more than 50% built) and the overall failure rate is then 40%.
- Average clutch size (eggs laid) was 4.37 for first clutch, 3.46 for second clutch and 3.0 for third.
- Average brood size (eggs hatched) was 3.55 for first brood and 2.83 for second.
- The average number of young fledging (leaving the nest) was 3.44 for first broods and 2.51 for second.
- Total number of young fledged was 327 and the average per pair, including those that failed to breed, was 2.67.
- 17 pairs made two breeding attempts in the same year, ten pairs (excluding 2001) made three. The number of extra breeding attempts in any year clearly reflects the nest failure rate.
- 21 pairs managed to raise a second brood. The number of pairs failing to breed varied considerably – from two in 2002 to nine in 2004.

Results – nest sites and habitat

During the survey other information was collected for each nest and is summarised thus:

- The average height of nests above ground level was 2.6m – the more extreme variations ranged from 0.5m to 5m, but most nests were sited within a range of 1.5m to 3.5m.
- Nests were built facing all aspects (north, south, east, west) with some in direct sun for at least part of the day.

- Most nests were sited on house walls, some on garden walls, several were against tree trunks and a few in open sheds.

- Most were in shrubs growing tightly against the wall. Virginia creeper, wisteria, vines, climbing hydrangea and climbing rose were most commonly used. Espalier pear and trimmed cotoneaster were selected occasionally. The nests were sited against the wall and supported by a horizontal branch. In a few cases, a fast-growing shrub such as a vine was selected, but as the growing tip extended so the extra weight caused the branch to tip, taking the nest with it – with disastrous results.

- A few nests were located in shallow holes in walls or in tree trunks.

- In several villages 'clumping' of pairs occurred with up to six pairs occupying an area 250m x 250m . In one village, a clump of six pairs occurred at one end of the village and another of three pairs at the other end. In one case, three pairs nested simultaneously on the same house. Yet what appeared to be suitable flycatcher habitat occurred throughout the village – indeed, some villagers remember birds nesting there in the past.

- The earliest arrival date was 10th May with most birds arriving in late May or early June.

- A few began nest building during the third and fourth weeks of May but most began during early June.

Comparisons with national data

The spreadsheet in the Appendix provides comparisons with long-term data held by the BTO. In this study the average nest failure rate appears to increase each year but the statistics need further explanation. True, 2003 and 2004 were the worst years but 2004 reflected the loss of seven broods from starvation, something that did not occur in the other three years. Excluding them the failure rate would have been 34.09% – better than 2003.

This provides a good illustration of how difficult it is to draw comparisons between this shorter survey and the statistics supplied by the BTO covering 1966-2003. Analysts would need to extract BTO data covering the same period as this study before a more direct comparison could be made. Meanwhile, the overall nest failure rate for this study of 34.6% is close to the BTO historical figure of 32.8%.

Similarly, average clutch and brood sizes provide some broad comparisons but the full picture is much more complicated. The BTO data does not distinguish between first, second and third clutches – or between first and second brood sizes. In this study, pairs whose nest failed were followed through successive attempts but it is unlikely that all BTO nest recorders could find the time required. As successive attempts produce fewer eggs and young (see data pages 68 & 69) it is likely that the overall averages for this study will be lower compared with the BTO data – and that proved to be the case. If the Constant Nest Monitoring Scheme develops to include other Spotted Flycatcher researchers then more accurate comparisons will be possible.

Comparisons with other parts of the UK

Over the past year or so I have been contacted by several people who have learned about the survey. Most are private individuals who know the Spotted Flycatcher well but some are members of small groups who have set up similar projects. I designed a recording form for those who might want to monitor their nests and send me the information. It was sad to find that in several instances, only when they looked for their flycatchers did they realise that the birds no longer nested there. This reflects the anecdotal information that I have collected around our villages – for the first time in years, many sites are no longer occupied, proof that supports nest record data from the wider countryside. However, quite a lot of information did come in and it is interesting to see the similarities – and differences – described. For instance, I am told that in Shropshire Spotted Flycatchers have often nested on the hinges of large gates. (Holloway pers. comm.) In Devon they are using open-fronted boxes sited in trees along a river bank. (Ovendon pers. comm.) In Scotland, where they still breed in trees on woodland edge and glades, the nest is built on a branch against the trunk (Shaw pers. comm.) – something that I've seen in yew trees in this survey area. They are reported in open-fronted farm buildings – including one in a National Trust shop! But the prize for the most unusual site should go to one recorded in the Norfolk Report (Warren) where a contributor reported a successful nest on a shelf in a dairy shop. The shop was open to the public and the nest site was a roll of Sellotape! However most reports are of birds nesting in cavities, nest-boxes and in climbing shrubs and creepers on buildings.

Only generalised comparisons with smaller or shorter-term surveys are possible. Nevertheless, it is clear that breeding success varies considerably between areas as well as years. For example, a small sample from the midlands area in 2004 (Caldwell) found that three nests produced 12 young with 100% hatching and fledging rates, considerably better results than any year from this study.

At the time of writing, outside this study area two others reported young dying of hypothermia or starvation in 2004. A study in Norfolk (Warren) cites the weather as the likely cause of several nest failures. The weather was also blamed for the loss of a brood in Herefordshire (Ovendon pers. comm.).

One contact in Yorkshire reported few birds turning up in local villages in 2004 and those that did appeared to leave after a couple of weeks (Warwick pers. comm.).

A report for a study in Norfolk in 2003/4 (Warren) indicated a slightly higher nest failure rate (35.5%) than this study (34.6%). A much smaller study in Herefordshire (Ovendon) reported only a 12.5% failure rate.

Conclusions

We should remind ourselves here that the original purpose of the survey was merely to assess the status of the Spotted Flycatcher in the local villages – and in that sense the project was a great success. Yes, flycatchers are alive and well in many of our 'traditional' villages.

However, thanks to the local support for the survey we can also say:

- 2002 was by far the best year of the survey for the birds – with more pairs, larger clutches of eggs and much higher numbers of young fledged per pair.
- Each year, despite a varying number of failures, the numbers of fledged young (leaving the nest) exceeded the number of breeding adults.

- Populations and breeding success appear to vary considerably from year to year – this survey ranging from 30 to 40 pairs, with average breeding success ranging from 2.27 to 3.68 young per pair.
- Without ringing the birds it is impossible to assert if some, or all, are site faithful – i.e. return year after year. The fact that unusually coloured eggs were found in two nests built by one pair at two neighbouring properties in one year – and that similarly marked eggs were found two years later in a nest less than 400m away – suggests that at least the adult female, or an offspring, returned. That Spotted Flycatchers use the remains of a previous flycatcher nest, often well hidden, as a base for their new one, may also indicate previous knowledge of an area. However, the fact that in 2004 two pairs bred in a village where none had been seen for a number of years would indicate that at least some birds move away from their natal area. Furthermore, despite maintaining the intensity of the searches for pairs (and allowing for the fact that inevitably one or two might be missed), numbers varied considerably – from 30 to 40 – over the four year period. This also indicates that at least some birds do not return to the same village every year – if at all. It could be assumed that after a really productive breeding year more birds would return the following spring. In this survey, 2002 was by far the most productive but it was followed by one of the two lowest breeding populations. It has been proved that at least some birds have bred well away from their natal area – two breeding adults ringed in Britain and Ireland were subsequently re-caught while breeding in Germany and Denmark (*The Migration Atlas*).
- Short periods of bad weather in 2004 caused the loss of seven entire broods of small young in the nest (none in earlier years), whilst many other species less dependant on

a very local population of flying insects fared much better. Within the period of this survey it might be easy to blame modern climate change. But the Spotted Flycatcher has long been particularly prone to such disasters. An excerpt from a bird magazine series published in the 1960s (no title) states that 'periods of inclement weather prevent them [flycatchers] from collecting food efficiently' and refers to 'many cases where some or all the young are found dead in the nest'. During a study into the feeding behaviour of six pairs, in 1974 and 1975, Davies observed that larger prey items were more likely to be fed to the nestlings but that in cold, wet conditions when larger prey items were unavailable, the adults rarely fed them. The broods of three of the study pairs died during one week of bad weather. In this respect at least, nothing appears to have changed since the 1960s. Perhaps we should not be too keen to blame the shortage of food on pesticides and global warming; with its higher dependence on flying insects the Spotted Flycatcher is more vulnerable to such disasters.

- Many pairs make up to three attempts to breed – a few building three nests and laying three clutches before succeeding. Most will try twice. Each year, up to 20% will breed twice but weather conditions and predation rates appear to influence this.

- It is clear that coconut shells as nest sites appear almost irresistible to Spotted Flycatchers. In this study, if there was an available shell within a chosen territory more often than not the birds would build there. This bears out findings in the 1940s (*The Birdman*) when all twenty pairs nesting against a wall used coconut shells.

- There is evidence to suggest that desertion, although quite rare, is most likely to occur at nest building stage. This may be caused directly by competition from other species, disturbance by predators or from gardening or building activity. There was very little evidence of desertion at egg stage and none at young stage.

- Only one adult was known to have died during the breeding season.
- From observations, the greatest threat of nest predation comes from grey squirrel and domestic cat, but nests were also predated by magpie, jackdaw and mouse. Nests were thought to have been damaged by house sparrow and woodpigeon.

We cannot say ...

- that from the data, the Spotted Flycatcher is declining in our villages – although anecdotal evidence suggests that it is.
- whether the current productivity (number of young fledged per pair) is sufficient to sustain local populations. Current average lifespan and annual mortality rates would be required before an assessment could be made.
- that clutch size influences breeding success – although this has been suggested from long-term studies of other species.

Questions raised and some answers

Q. Did monitoring of nests cause any to be lost to predators?

A. Possibly, but certainly not noticeably – there is no way of checking. However, I assume that it may have happened on rare occasions and this has to be considered when planning a project. In this case I feel that any danger was far outweighed because the survey and monitoring increased public awareness of the birds' breeding requirements, leading to changes (for example, in timing of gardening or house maintenance work) that meant some nests succeeded where they would otherwise have failed.

Q. Do certain nest box designs attract more predators?

A. The survey was too short – particularly as large numbers of nest-boxes were not put up until 2003. Spotted Flycatchers seem inexplicably drawn to half coconut shells sited in suitable positions. Because predators are attracted increasingly to local gardens it is possible that they may make regular checks of nest-boxes. The predation rate of the boxes does seem high and perhaps the design should be modified to provide just a coconut shell and at most, a back-plate.

Q. Should the survey continue?

A. Yes and no! Yes, it would be better to have data from ten or even twenty years but in practical terms this would not be possible and so it is likely that a compromise situation will evolve. In order to build on what has already been collected a modified survey would have to be comparable with at least part of the original.

Selected Observations

As mentioned earlier, over the four years I and other contributors to the study have collected many observations and some are listed here:

At one site the male flycatcher was observed as it caught a bee before flying back to a perch. Once there it began to wipe/beat the insect on the branch to remove the wings and the sting. He was joined by the female, who had been watching from the nest and she began to beg by quivering her wings and posturing. The male fluttered above her, briefly landing on her back as though to mate – and passed over the bee. The female repeated the ritual of beating and wiping the bee on the branch before finally eating it.

I touched on the subject of feeding behaviour earlier (The Bird – The Breeding Season). The hours spent watching the birds collecting food in order to locate their nest site can provide useful observations about their feeding behaviour – for example, that they took few 'white' butterflies until later in the season. On one occasion I watched as a bird returned from a feeding trip to my neighbour's buddleia bush. When it landed I could identify clearly a marbled white butterfly (*Melanargia* galathea) in its bill. This was the first and only record for the species in the area around our house! During several sunny days when our buddleia was in bloom, the

Spotted Flycatcher perched on the top of the bush and targeted a large species of day-flying moth – possibly the Silver Y (*Autographa gamma*), a number of which it fed (minus wings) to the nestlings.

It became clear at an early stage that the changeable nature of the British weather must surely affect Spotted Flycatcher breeding success. So heavily reliant on flying insects within a short distance of the nest, in colder, wet and windy weather the birds' choice of prey becomes extremely limited. Observations showed that on warm, sunny days the birds would feed in the open – from the tops of trees and television aerials down to fences, clothes lines and even croquet hoops. From this variety of perches they found apparently abundant prey. However, during bad weather the birds were much harder to find – feeding beneath the dense canopy of trees, using the lower branches or ground plants and fences as perches – and sometimes up in the canopy itself. Furthermore, even with binoculars it was difficult to see what they caught – most items appeared to be much smaller than a house fly. Clearly, it would take many more small items of prey to feed a brood – or the adults.

Spotted Flycatchers appear to be selective – especially in times of plenty, when they were observed to ignore a number of chances to catch prey passing quite close to them.

Observations also showed that the adult birds rarely fed far from their nest and usually within 20m or so. This strategy must reduce the time needed to return to the nest and therefore increase the time spent foraging or hunting. Indeed, this behaviour was recorded in great detail by Davies – one pair, apparently feeding within a 180 degree arc from the nest on a house wall, took almost 70% of their prey from perches sited within 25m of the nest.

Photo Courtesy Faith Hallett

Apparently, a youngster's gape (how wide it opens its mouth!) is wider than that of an adult. Consequently the adults are more likely to pass larger prey to their young (Davies).

In 2002 I attempted to record flycatcher feeding conditions from day to day by assessing the availability of their food. Rather grandly, I thought of calling it 'VAFF' or the 'Visual Availability of Flycatcher Food'! However, the title was unimportant – I needed a simple way of assessing the daily situation. I chose a scale of nought to five to indicate the relative abundance of food and each day during my rounds of the villages I estimated the general conditions. The experiment ran from the 20th May to the 7th August and the daily notes were transcribed onto a chart. It showed clearly that food availability varied a great deal Only a few days in May scored zero, there were periods of several days when the score stayed at three or under and other times when food was abundant for up to a week. I tried to relate these findings to the success or failure of various nests but soon realised the complexity of such comparisons and the need to continue the trials for several years.

One pair was observed refurbishing their nest 10 days after the first brood fledged. On several occasions during visits to the nest, the female was accompanied by a youngster. During incubation the male bird was missing for several days but was located nearby, feeding fledged young. Later he returned to the nest area, still occasionally feeding a youngster (30 days after fledging). The following day he drove away the young bird and on the next day the second clutch hatched and he began to provision the new brood.

The bravery of Spotted Flycatchers in defending their nests has been noted before (*BWP*). On one occasion I was almost struck by a bird (within a few centimetres), as I approached a nest where the young were within a few days of fledging.

Long-suspected of predating Spotted Flycatcher nests, a grey squirrel was actually watched by me as it ate the eggs whilst the adults watched helplessly.

A Spotted Flycatcher made a sustained attack on a grey squirrel that came too near to the nest. The squirrel made three attempts to climb a nearby plum tree but each time was forced to descend, finally making its escape across a lawn and into a tree some 50m away. Similar instances have been reported, (*BWP*). Local observers agree that the birds become increasingly noisy and aggressive as their young approach fledging.

I watched another pair of flycatchers attacking a grey squirrel near their nest. The animal had approached along the top of a 2 m high wall. The birds constantly harried it by diving vertically from several metres. Eventually, one bird actually struck the squirrel – it was not clear whether with beak or claw but the result was dramatic. The animal seemed to convulse and then ran at full speed for the cover of an overhanging shrub, where it groomed itself for a few minutes before creeping away.

Watching them perched in prominent positions, I had often wondered how vulnerable the Spotted Flycatcher adult is to predation, and then one day I got an answer. I was hidden in a large garden and watching a bird feeding from a perch on a dead twig at the top of a tree – some ten metres above the ground and completely exposed. It made repeated sallies to grab insects around the top of the tree and I kept my binoculars trained on it, hoping that it would eventually head back to a nest. Suddenly, and quite dramatically, it dropped vertically from the twig into the foliage of the tree and as it did so a sparrowhawk (*Accipiter nisus*) hurtled past – about a metre above. From that moment I decided that because the flycatchers are constantly scanning for flying prey when perched in such places, they have a far greater chance of seeing the attacker and taking avoiding action. I have no reason to believe that any adults in the study were killed by sparrowhawk.

At one property, urgent building works necessitated the cutting back of a vine to install a drainage down-pipe. Seeing the occupied nest-box the gardener hurriedly took it down and re-positioned it several metres to one side. As he walked away with the ladder the bird returned, located her nest and resumed sitting!

A nest in a coconut shell on the wall of a house was 80% completed when the builders arrived to carry out roof repairs that required scaffolding. The birds disappeared and despite searches by the house-owner and me, were not found. After two weeks the scaffolding was removed and within a few hours the birds (surely the same pair?) resumed building.

The loss of young broods as a direct result of spells of bad weather had been suspected before. On three occasions in 2004 I found evidence of this – and indeed evidence that adults remove small, dead young. Below the empty nest (or with one dead young remaining) I found the rest of the brood. The difference in sizes and various stages of decomposition suggested that they had died over a period of days – presumably from starvation rather than from hypothermia.

At one site, a pair was seen commencing nest building on 10th May – the earliest nest record for this study. However, in a stop/start way it took them until 3rd June to complete the nest. During that time they would disappear for up to a day, presumably looking for food. On 31st May the house-owner found the nest on the ground beneath the coconut shell box. It is thought that house sparrows had pulled out the material whilst building their own nest nearby. She quickly replaced the nest and the flycatchers resumed building later in the day. The birds appeared doomed to failure as later on the young, desperately begging for food were clearly in danger of knocking each other off the nest. Once again the house-owner stepped in, placing a wicker basket lined with a blanket just below the nest. On two occasions a youngster was found in the basket and each time it was revived and replaced in the nest. All four young eventually fledged over a period of two days, the smallest seen to fly up into a nearby tree to join its waiting siblings. The date was 5th July – some 57 days after nest building began! They did not attempt a second brood!

At one site a single egg hatched from a clutch of four. The hatching date was 16 days after the last egg laying date – the average is 12-14 days. However the youngster fledged after 10 days, two to four days earlier than the average.

Jackdaws almost certainly predated several flycatcher nests. These predators nest in chimneys of houses now converted to central heating. It would appear that the young jackdaws reach the fledging/post fledging period at the time when Spotted Flycatchers are starting to nest. Perched on rooftops the adults have a clear view of the gardens below. Jackdaws have been seen killing freshly fledged robins, blackbirds and thrushes in gardens. Once the post-fledging groups and flocks of jackdaw have moved away (usually to local farmland where they predate nests of breeding waders), the incidence of nest predation noticeably drops. Some house owners are wiring off their chimney pots to prevent access by these birds.

Several members of the Flycatcher Gang took it upon themselves to carry out culling of predators such as grey squirrel and magpie. 'Catch 'em alive' traps at two large gardens took 14 and 11 magpies respectively. I make no comment save my surprise to find that so many people were keen to deter or reduce predator numbers – or indeed that magpies occurred in such densities.

A failed nest from a coconut shell was removed and checked. The wall thickness was an average of 1.5cm – increasing to 1.8cm at the 'lip'. It was estimated that the material used amounted to 60-70% of that found in a 'natural' nest. This may explain why Spotted Flycatchers, which arrive quite late in the British breeding season, select the shells – clearly they can save precious time and energy.

One pair (out of two in that village) nested precisely in a site that had been used for eight years during the 1990s but which had been unoccupied for the past four.

Spotted Flycatchers have been reported feeding much later than other diurnal birds – often well after corvid and thrush species have gone to roost. In late August I watched a bird still feeding when it was too dark to see it perching – it was only visible when it flew up and was silhouetted against the sky. Its only companion was a bat!

At one site house sparrows usurped Spotted Flycatchers attempting to build in a box where they had nested for several years. Once the flycatchers had moved on, the sparrows abandoned the box.

The Future

For the Birds

In our area the Spotted Flycatcher no longer nests out in the wider countryside, but within the local Cotswold villages the bird is well known and certainly much loved. 2004 saw the return – or arrival – of thirty-seven pairs that chose to breed here. And there is plenty of room for more, perhaps several times that number. However, there may be an abundance of nesting habitat but is there enough food not only to nourish the adults but also to produce enough young to sustain or increase the population? We are told that populations of butterflies, moths, hoverflies and bees have fallen and it is likely that so too have numbers of other flycatcher prey species.

We know that millions of migrating birds (flycatchers among them) are being killed each year – for sport, for cage birds and to eat). Many of those trapping and shooting them are in European Union countries. The birds may also be suffering heavier mortality rates during migration, due to changes in climate and habitat loss along their way. If that were the case then there would be three main factors affecting their future. If our observations that more predators are drawn to local gardens are correct then that adds a fourth – worrying times indeed for the birds and for their supporters.

Clearly our survey has identified possibilities for further research:

- There is more to be learned about site fidelity – are males or females more likely to return to the natal area? Even if they are not always site faithful, do they return at least once during their lifetime?
- How does our village data compare with birds using more natural or semi-natural habitats – in woodland, parkland, scrub etc? Indeed, how does the British data compare with other European populations?
- How does our data compare with long-term research in other areas of Britain?
- Is there a significant loss of insect prey within the villages and can we reverse the situation?
- How can we get Spotted Flycatchers back into the natural habitats that they have left?
- Can anything be done to reduce the annual killing and taking of birds by man along migration routes?

For the People

None of the people involved in this project appear indifferent to the plight of the birds, and regardless of the project, they are concerned for their welfare. Many have decided to take positive action towards improving the breeding success, and more will do so. This could be achieved in several ways:

- By providing suitable nesting habitat.
- By ensuring that work on houses or in gardens causes minimal disturbance to the birds – at the nest or feeding.

Nest-boxes, where carefully sited, provide safe places for Spotted Flycatcher nests. This box has been used successfully for several years. However, in 2003 house sparrows drove off the flycatchers but did not use the box themselves – a good example of the fierce competition encountered by these late arrivals.

- As far as is practical (and legal!) by deterring predators. For example, wiring off chimneys to prevent jackdaws from nesting.
- By endeavouring to manage gardens to attract more insects – action that would also help other wildlife.
- By making others aware of the importance of gardens to wildlife and of the fact that for some species in our area the garden is now the only suitable habitat.
- By removing or modifying any nest-box that seems at risk from predators or of being disturbed.

For the Project

The effort required to continue the survey at the present levels is unsustainable. Therefore two questions must be resolved – should it continue at all, and if so, at what level? Local support for continuing is high and it has already been suggested that a longer-term survey would provide additional, important data. It may be that we need to reduce the size of the survey to cover a few known 'clumps' of pairs within the villages – and try to cut back on the number of nest visits. Perhaps some villagers would like to monitor their own nests (of their birds, that is!) as people in other parts of the country are doing, and then send in their data for inclusion or comparison.

It would be good to continue to work with other researchers elsewhere in Britain – and to find out more about the birds during migration and in the winter quarters. Perhaps a countrywide comparative study could be established, to which this and other studies could contribute. It has been suggested that a 'Smart Group' of Spotted Flycatcher researchers could be set up to provide a web-based discussion and information forum.

Meanwhile, the author and his wife will be contemplating the prospect of their first spring/summer holiday in many years!

Appendix, Acknowledgements and Bibliography

Appendix

The data

The spreadsheet contains summaries of the nest record data collected each year. This allows comparison between years. Then totals are provided and these can then be compared with the national statistics provided by the British Trust for Ornithology, which can draw on almost 12,000 nest records for Spotted Flycatcher – submitted by members over some 65 years.

What the spreadsheet shows clearly is that the bird is still widespread and breeding regularly in the villages.

The research does not prove whether or not the local populations of Spotted Flycatcher are in decline – as there is no earlier specific research with which to compare, the results must be seen as a 'snapshot' of current status.

Other data

The survey provided other data about the Spotted Flycatcher breeding ecology. Information was collected about nest material, nest height, aspect and position and used within the main body of the text – in 'Results, Comparisons and Conclusions: Results – nest sites and habitat'.

The data for each village can be identified, thus allowing other comparisons to be made. For instance, there is evidence that breeding success and nest failure/predation rates varied consistently between villages. For example, between the four local villages that contain most of the population studied, average failure/predation rates varied from 28.6% to 50%. The range of failure/predation rates for the four years and four villages was nil to 72.7%. More research is required before explanations are possible.

The data raises some interesting questions and these are discussed in 'Results, Comparisons and Conclusions: Questions raised'. Information from observers elsewhere in the country allows for some comparisons but suggests that a wider comparative study is desirable.

We know that within the villages 'clumping' of pairs occurs, despite the widespread availability of what appears to be suitable habitat. A more scientific study might provide reasons for this.

Spotted Flycatcher Data

Year	No. of pairs		No. of nests		Failed/predated				Average		
	found	studied	found	studied	nest	egg	young	died	Clutch size		
									1st	2nd	3rd
2001	30	30	33	33	1	3	4	nil	4.38	3.5	nil
2002	40	31	50	44	2	5	5	nil	4.56	3.42	3
2003	30	28	43	39	4	8	6	nil	4.17	3.64	3
2004	37	33	56	54	7	13	3	7	4.41	3.28	3
Totals	137	122	182	170	14	29	18	7	4.37	3.46	3
BTO	data	n/a	n/a	n/a	n/a	n/a	n/a	n/a	n/a	n/a	n/a

Year	Total no. of young fledged	Av. no. young per pair inc. failed pairs	Av. Nest failure rate - exc. nest stage	Overall av. clutch size
2001	73	2.43	21.87%	4.09
2002	114	3.68	23.81%	4.07
2003	65	2.32	40.00%	3.86
2004	75	2.27	48.93%	4.1
Overall	327	2.67	34.60%	4.03
BTO	Data n/a	n/a	32.80%	4.25

2001 - 2004

Year	Average Brood size		Fledglings per brood		Breeding Attempts		second broods	No. pairs failing to breed
	1st	2nd	1st	2nd	2	3		
2001	3.31	2.71	3.12	2.33	4	NA	6	NA
2002	4.48	3.07	3.94	2.78	2	3	6	2
2003	3.23	2.91	3.21	2.44	3	3	5	8
2004	3.48	2.62	3.5	2.5	8	4	4	9
Totals	3.55	2.83	3.44	2.51	n/a	n/a	n/a	n/a
BTO	n/a	n/a	n/a	n/a	n/a	n/a	n/a	n/a

Year	Overall av. brood size
2001	2.2
2002	3.9
2003	3.92
2004	3.26
Overall	3.32
BTO	3.72

Acknowledgements

There is not enough room here to thank everyone in the villages who has supported or contributed to the survey. Most did what they could, a few made outstanding efforts. Most of the community know very well who they are, but their names would mean nothing to people from elsewhere. So, John, Georgina, Fred, Ros, Mary – and so many others – you remain anonymous but no less important to me and to the survey. My wife Pamela will not be allowed such anonymity. She has supported, encouraged and helped throughout the project and also proof-read several drafts of the text.

When I decided to try to write this book I had no knowledge of modern publishing and no funding. One of the project's supporters suggested that I ask for advice on a small, local website. Once again the response was amazing, with offers of training, advice, contacts and help. Most importantly, Plum Tree Publishing Ltd took on all the technical and organisational aspects, leaving me free to write the text.

My area-wide search for a cartoonist to produce the front cover ended in a nearby village. Brian Smith is not only a wonderful artist and cartoonist but he turned out to be a fan of the Spotted Flycatcher as well!

Members of the local community and two BTO members offered pictures and these are individually acknowledged.

I am grateful to Sue Coleman, Gordon Hutchins and several others who have kindly given up their time to proof-read the text.

Humphrey Crick, Chris Hewson and Dave Leech of the British Trust for Ornithology supplied advice, data and other information.

Kester Wilson provided comments on migration from the British coast. Simon Holloway and Geoff Shaw provided information on nest sites. Nick Ovendon, Dave Caldwell and Rachel Warren generously shared their nest data with me. Jill Warwick sent observations.

Despite all of the help and encouragement acknowledged above, this book would still not have been published without the generosity of some of the local community. Several people offered sponsorship – by far the largest contribution came from someone who promised to underwrite any shortfall. Typically, they wish to remain anonymous. "Thank you" will never be enough.

Bibliography

Cramp, S., Perrins, C.M., et al, editors, *Handbook of the Birds of Europe the Middle East and North Africa: The Birds of the Western Palearctic*, vol. VII (Oxford: Oxford University Press, 1993)

Davies, N.B., 'Prey Selection and the Search Strategy of the Spotted Flycatcher (*Muscicapa striata*): A Field Study on Optimal Foraging', *Animal Behaviour*, 25 (1977), 1016-1033

Douglas-Home, H., *The Birdman*, edited by J McEwen. (London: Collins, 1977)

Fuller, R.J., *Bird Habitats in Britain* (Calton: Poyser, 1982)

Maclean, G.L., *Roberts' Birds of Southern Africa*, 6th Edition (London: New Holland, 1993)

O'Connor, J.O., and M. Shrubb, *Farming and Birds* (Cambridge: Cambridge University Press, 1986)

Warren, R., 'Norfolk Spotted Flycatcher Project: - Summary. 2003-4'. (private publication)

Wernham, C., M. Toms, J. Marchant, J. Clark, G. Siriwardena, and S. Baillie, editors *The Migration Atlas: Movements of the birds of Britain and Ireland* (London: Poyser, 2003)

'Warning'

Too much research may damage
your health!